Sunshine on My Shoulders

Description

Learners observe the phenomenon of "mystery bead" bracelets changing colors when they go outdoors and conduct simple investigations to find out what makes the beads change color. They discover that invisible rays of ultraviolet (UV) light cause the beads to change color. They learn about the benefits of the Sun, as well as the harmful effects of too much sunlight on their skin, and they test the effectiveness of sunscreen on UV beads. Finally, learners create a sun safety poster.

Alignment With the *Next Generation Science Standards*

Performance Expectations

K-PS3-1: Make observations to determine the effect of sunlight on Earth's surface.

K-2-ETS1-1: Ask questions, make observations, and gather information about a situation people want to change to define a simple problem that can be solved through the development of a new or improved object or tool.

Science and Engineering Practices	Disciplinary Core Ideas	Crosscutting Concept
Planning and Carrying Out Investigations With guidance, plan and conduct an investigation in collaboration with peers. Evaluate different ways of observing and/or measuring a phenomenon to determine which way can answer a question. **Analyzing and Interpreting Data** Record information (observations, thoughts, and ideas). Use observations (firsthand or from media) to describe patterns and/or relationships in the natural and designed world(s) in order to answer scientific questions and solve problems. Analyze data from tests of an object or tool to determine if it works as intended.	**PS3.B: Conservation of Energy and Energy Transfer** Sunlight warms Earth's surface. **ETS1.A: Defining and Delimiting Engineering Problems** A situation that people want to change or create can be approached as a problem to be solved through engineering. Such problems may have many acceptable solutions.	**Cause and Effect** Simple tests can be designed to gather evidence to support or refute student ideas about causes.

Continued

Alignment With the Next Generation Science Standards *(continued)*

Science and Engineering Practices	Disciplinary Core Ideas	Crosscutting Concept
Obtaining, Evaluating, and Communicating Information Read grade-appropriate texts and/or use media to obtain scientific and/or technical information to determine patterns in and/or evidence about the natural and designed world(s). Communicate information or design ideas and/or solutions with others in oral and/or written forms using models, drawings, writing, or numbers that provide detail about scientific ideas, practices, and/or design ideas.		

Note: The activities in this lesson will help students move toward the performance expectations listed, which is the goal after multiple activities. However, the activities will not by themselves be sufficient to reach the performance expectations.

Featured Picture Books

TITLE: ***Sun***
AUTHOR: **Marion Dane Bauer**
ILLUSTRATOR: **John Wallace**
PUBLISHER: **Simon Spotlight**
YEAR: **2016**
GENRE: **Non-Narrative Information**
SUMMARY: *This Ready-to-Read Level 1 book explains that the Sun is a star and that it gives Earth the heat and light that we need.*

TITLE: ***Sunshine on My Shoulders***
AUTHOR: **John Denver**
ILLUSTRATOR: **Christopher Canyon**
PUBLISHER: **Dawn Publications**
YEAR: **2003**
GENRE: **Story**
SUMMARY: *This picture book adaptation of John Denver's song "Sunshine on My Shoulders" celebrates the simple things in life such as sunshine, nature, and loving relationships.*

Time Needed

This lesson will take several class periods. Suggested scheduling is as follows:

Session 1: **Engage** with Mystery Beads and What Do You Think Made the Beads Change Color?

Session 2: **Explore** with Mystery Bead Investigations and **Explain** with Sunlight Is Special

Session 3: **Explain** with *Sun* Read-Aloud and Thank-You Note to the Sun

Session 4: **Elaborate** with *Sunshine on My Shoulders* Read-Aloud and Sunscreen Test

Session 5: **Evaluate** with Sun Safety Tips

Materials

- UV beads (5 per student)
- Pipe cleaners or long twist ties (1 per student)
- Crayons or colored pencils
- 1 bottle of sunscreen (at least SPF 30)
- 2 small zipper baggies

UV beads are available from

Steve Spangler Science
www.stevespanglerscience.com

Educational Innovations, Inc.
www.teachersource.com

Amazon.com

Student Pages

- Mystery Beads Booklet
- Thank You, Sun!
- Sun Safety Tip
- STEM Everywhere

Background for Teachers

SAFETY

When taking students outdoors, remind them to never look directly at the Sun. Looking at the Sun can damage their eyes.

In this lesson, students dive deep into the science and engineering practices (SEPs) of planning and carrying out investigations and analyzing and interpreting data as they explore the effects of the Sun's energy on Earth. They are guided through these practices step by step as they investigate why the "mystery beads" they are given change color when they go outside. Applying the crosscutting concept (CCC) of cause and effect, they generate possible causes for the color change, plan and carry out simple investigations to test each explanation, and record data for each test. The *Framework* suggests that in the elementary years, students' experiences should be structured to help them learn how to conduct a fair investigation, how to decide what data to record, and how to support a claim with evidence. In this lesson, the question is provided by the phenomenon of the color-changing beads and the investigations are guided by the teacher, but in the upper grades, students will begin investigating their own questions and designing their own investigations. These early experiences lay the foundation for what is ahead.

Radiation from the Sun, or sunlight, is actually a mixture of different kinds of light, including infrared light, visible light, and ultraviolet (UV) light. In this lesson, students learn about the benefits of sunlight, such as heat and light, as well as the harmful effects that UV light can have on their skin. They learn that UV color-changing beads are handy inventions for detecting UV light. The plastic beads used in this lesson contain a pigment that changes color when exposed to UV radiation. The beads are white in ordinary, visible light but in UV light, you'll see different colors depending on the pigment added to each bead. Skin is also a detector of UV light. When bare skin is exposed to sunlight, it becomes darker (suntan) or redder (sunburn). These responses by the skin are a signal that the cells under the skin are being assaulted by UV radiation from the Sun. UV radiation breaks chemical bonds in skin tissue and over prolonged exposure, skin may wrinkle or skin cancer may develop.

The problem of sunlight damaging skin can be solved through engineering. One solution is sunscreen, invented more than 80 years ago. Sunscreen can help you enjoy sunlight by preventing some of the Sun's UV light from reaching your skin, by either reflecting or absorbing these rays. In the Elaborate portion of the lesson, students test the effects of putting sunscreen on the UV beads. They learn that sunscreen can keep some UV light from reaching the beads, and that it can help protect your skin in the same way. The Sun Protection Factor, or SPF, is a number (4, 15, 30, etc.) that tells you how long the Sun's UV light rays would take to redden your skin if you apply the sunscreen as directed compared with the amount of time without sunscreen. So, if you use a sunscreen with an SPF of 30 as directed, it would take you 30 times longer to burn than if you used no sunscreen. In the STEM Everywhere portion of this lesson, students watch a video to learn about SPF and how it can be tested using color-changing bottles. For more information on Sun safety, see the "Websites" section.

Learning Progressions

Below are the DCI grade band endpoints for grades K–2 and 3–5. These are provided to show how student understanding of the DCIs in this lesson will progress in future grade levels.

DCIs	Grades K–2	Grades 3–5
PS3.B: Conservation of Energy and Energy Transfer	• Sunlight warms Earth's surface.	• Light also transfers energy from place to place.
ETS1.A: Defining and Delimiting Engineering Problems	• A situation that people want to change or create can be approached as a problem to be solved through engineering. Such problems may have many acceptable solutions.	• Possible solutions to a problem are limited by available materials and resources (constraints). The success of a designed solution is determined by considering the desired features of a solution (criteria). Different proposals for solutions can be compared on the basis of how well each one meets the specified criteria for success or how well each takes the constraints into account.

Source: Willard, T., ed. 2015. *The NSTA quick-reference guide to the* NGSS: *Elementary school.* Arlington, VA: NSTA Press.

engage

Mystery Beads

This part of the lesson is best done on a sunny day. Students will be making bracelets with UV beads that change color in sunlight. To keep the color change a secret, tell them only that they are going to make a "mystery bead" bracelet today. Model how to make the bracelet by stringing five UV beads on a pipe cleaner (or long twist tie). You can use this opportunity to count aloud together as you count out the beads. Give each student a pipe cleaner and five beads. When students have the beads on their bracelets, help them twist their bracelets on their wrists. Then, explain that you are going to take them outside to play, and that they should pay close attention to any changes in their bracelets. Next, go outside.

The students will be surprised and excited when their beads change color in sunlight, but *do not tell students the reason for the change yet.* When they come back into the classroom, give them a copy of the Mystery Beads booklet. Ask them to promptly color the picture of the beads on the first page (because the beads will slowly change back to white when you're inside). You may want to have crayons and copies of the Mystery Beads booklet available outside so that students don't have to wait to color their beads.

What Do You Think Made the Beads Change Color?

Turn and Talk

When students are finished coloring, *ask*

? What did you notice when you went outside with your bracelets on?

? What are you wondering?

? Why do you think the beads changed color? (Have them share their ideas with a partner.) Possible student responses may include

- The hot or cold air made them change.
- The water in the air made them change.
- The wind made them change.
- The bright light made them change.

Record the possible causes for the color change on the board. After the discussion, have students turn to page 2 (What Do You Think Made the Beads Change Color?) of their booklet and write or draw what they think caused the color change in the beads.

OBSERVING THE MYSTERY BEADS

> **CCC: Cause and Effect**
> Simple tests can be designed to gather evidence to support or refute student ideas about causes.

Ask

? How can we find out for sure what causes the beads to change color outside? (We can test our ideas one by one.)

explore

Mystery Bead Investigations

Have students turn to page 3 ("Mystery Bead Investigations") in their Mystery Bead booklets. If possible, project the data table from that page. Tell students that a table is a good way to keep track of tests and results. Read the title of the first column "Possible Cause" and read through the list of explanations. Then read the title of the second column, "Did the Beads Change Color?" Tell students that you are going to test each possible cause together.

Mystery Bead Investigations

Possible Cause	Did the Beads Change Color? Yes or No (Circle)
Heat	
Bright Light	
Water	
Cold	
Wind	
The Sun	

SEP: Planning and Carrying Out Investigations
Evaluate different ways of observing and/or measuring a phenomenon to determine which way can answer a question.

With guidance, plan and conduct an investigation in collaboration with peers.

SEP: Analyzing and Interpreting Data
Record information.

For each one, *ask*

? How could we test whether this cause made the beads change color?

Have students discuss each way of testing the color change in the beads and evaluate which ways might work.

Below are some examples of simple tests for each possible cause.

Possible Cause	**Recommended Test**
The *heat* made the beads change.	Hold the bracelet tight in your hand to warm it up.
The *bright light* made them change.	Hold the beads under a bright lamp.
The *water* in the air made the beads change.	Dip the beads in water or spray them with water.
The *cold* made the beads change.	Put an ice cube on the beads.
The *wind* made the beads change.	Hold the beads in front of a fan.
Something special about the *Sun* made them change.	Hold the beads in the sunlight.

Perform each test. Some tests, such as the "heat" test, will be easy for each student to perform on their own bead bracelets. Other tests, such as the "cold" test, could be done as a demonstration. After each test, have students circle the thumbs-up or thumbs-down sign in the data table for that test. After all the tests have been completed and the data recorded, have students review their data tables. *Ask*

? What is the only test where our answer was yes/thumbs-up? (the Sun)

Explain that the investigations showed that none of the other possible causes made the beads change color. So, there must be something special about sunlight that affects the beads' color.

explain

Sunlight Is Special

Connecting to the Common Core
Reading: Informational Text
Key Ideas and Details: K.2

Have students turn to page 4 of their Mystery Beads booklet, titled "Sunlight Is Special." If possible, project that page. Tell students that you are going to read the page aloud and you would like them to follow along and listen for the reason the beads changed color in sunlight.

Monitoring Comprehension

After the first paragraph pause to model how good readers monitor their comprehension by verbalizing your "inner conversation." You might say, "I don't get this part; I am going to reread it," or "Wow, I never knew there are some kinds of light you can't see!"

After reading the "Sunlight Is Special" page, *ask*

? Based on what we just read, what caused the mystery beads to change color outdoors? (UV light)

? Where does UV light come from? (the Sun)

? What can UV light do to your skin? (give you a sunburn)

Tell students that they can take their bracelets and their booklets home. Challenge them to use these materials to teach someone at home about how sunlight affects the mystery beads.

Sun Read-Aloud

Connecting to the Common Core
Reading: Informational Text
Key Ideas and Details: K.2

Determining Importance

Show students the cover of the book *Sun*. Tell students that as you read this book aloud, you would like them to signal when they hear something good that we get from the Sun. You may want to teach the American Sign Language sign for Sun, and have students use it for their signal. Show students that to sign the first part of "Sun," you make a circle with your index finger near the top of your head. For the second part, start with your fingers and thumb together and then spread them apart like the Sun is shining down on you. For video demonstrations of the various ways to sign "Sun," see the "Websites" section at the end of this chapter.

Then read the book aloud.

SEP: Obtaining, Evaluating, and Communicating Information
Read grade-appropriate texts to obtain scientific information to determine patterns in and/or evidence about the designed world.

Turn and Talk

After reading the last page, which reads, "Thank you, Sun!," *ask*

? Why is the author saying "thank you" to the Sun?

? What good things do we get from the Sun?

Have students turn and talk to a neighbor to share the good things we get from the Sun. Then refer back to the following pages:

- Page 6: The Sun gives us light.
- Page 8: The Sun warms us.
- Pages 20–26: It warms Earth's water.
- Page 28: It helps our bodies make Vitamin D to keep our bones strong.

Thank-You Note to the Sun

Connecting to the Common Core
Writing
Text Types and Purposes: K.2

Writing

Give each student a copy of the Thank You, Sun! student page. Tell them that they are going to write a thank-you note to the Sun for the good things it gives us. Explain that a thank-you note is normally written to a person, but it will be fun to write one to the Sun to show what they have learned. Explain that thank-you notes usually begin with "Dear" and then a person's name, and that it is important to include what you are thanking the person for. So, the first line of the note reads, "Thank you for ..." and then students can fill in the rest of the note. Ask them for ideas on what they might write. You may want to write some key words or phrases on the board. At the end of the note, they should sign their name. In the box, they can draw a picture of something they like to do in the sunshine.

SEP: Obtaining, Evaluating, and Communicating Information
Communicate information with others in oral and/or written forms using drawings or writing that provide detail about scientific ideas.

Sunshine on My Shoulders sing-along

elaborate

Sunshine on My Shoulders Read-Aloud and Sunscreen Test

Connecting to the Common Core
Reading: Literature
Craft and Structure: K.6

Making Connections: Text to Self

Show students the cover of the book *Sunshine on My Shoulders. Ask*

? How does it make you feel to have the Sun shining on your shoulders?

Tell students that the book you will read to them is actually a song written by John Denver. He believed that the most wonderful things in life are simple and free, like sunshine and friendship. An artist by the name of Christopher Canyon created pictures to go along with the song. You may want to play the CD (enclosed in the hardcover version of the book), download an audio version, or sing

the lyrics as you show students the pictures. Invite students to sing along.

After singing, *ask*

- ? What are some good things about sunshine? (Answers might include it gives us light, it warms the earth, it makes plants grow, it makes us feel good, and so on.)
- ? What are some harmful things about sunshine? (It can burn your skin and damage your eyes.)
- ? Have you ever had a sunburn? How did it make you feel? (Answers will vary.)
- ? What are some things that people have invented to protect skin and eyes from sunshine? (Answers will vary, but may include hats, sunglasses, sunblock, sunscreen, umbrellas, or sun-protective clothing.)

> **SEP: Planning and Carrying Out Investigations**
> With guidance, plan and conduct an investigation in collaboration with peers.
>
> **SEP: Analyzing and Interpreting Data**
> Analyze data from tests of an object or tool to determine if it works as intended.

Revisit the illustration on pages 9 and 10 of *Sun* and *ask*

- ? What ways are the children in the illustration protecting their skin from UV light from the Sun? (wearing a hat, sitting in the shade of an umbrella, wearing sunglasses, putting on sunscreen)
- ? Why do we wear sunscreen outdoors? (Answers may vary.)

Explain that sunscreen was invented more than 80 years ago as a solution to the problem of sunlight damaging our skin. Sunscreen protects skin from the UV light from the Sun.

Ask

- ? What do you think would happen if we put sunscreen on the UV beads?
- ? How could we test this question?

After discussing and evaluating the students' ideas, choose one idea or carry out this procedure:

1. Place several of the UV beads into two zipper baggies.
2. Generously coat one side of one of the baggies with sunscreen (SPF 30 or higher).
3. Leave the other baggie uncoated as a control, so students can compare the effect of sunlight on the beads with and without sunscreen.
4. Take both baggies into the sun and let them sit for about 5 minutes.
5. Have students observe and compare.

> **CCC: Cause and Effect**
> Simple tests can be designed to gather evidence to support or refute student ideas about causes.

The UV beads with sunscreen will appear very faint in color compared to the bright colors of the UV beads without sunscreen. *Ask* students

- ? What do you observe? (The UV beads with sunscreen are lighter in color.)
- ? So, did the sunscreen work? (yes)
- ? How do you know? (The beads with sunscreen didn't get as dark.)
- ? Do you think the sunscreen blocks all the UV light? (No, because the beads with sunscreen did turn color slightly. The sunscreen blocks only some UV light.)
- ? What are you still wondering? (Answers will vary.)

Discuss the students' experiences with using sunscreen. Explain that they should use it when they are in the sun for a prolonged period of time, even on cloudy days, because it does a good job of keeping harmful UV light from damaging our

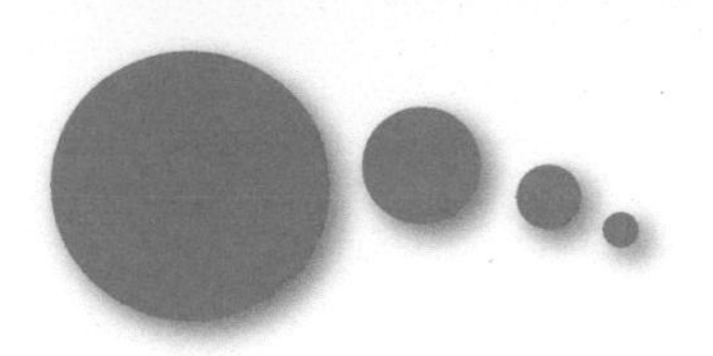

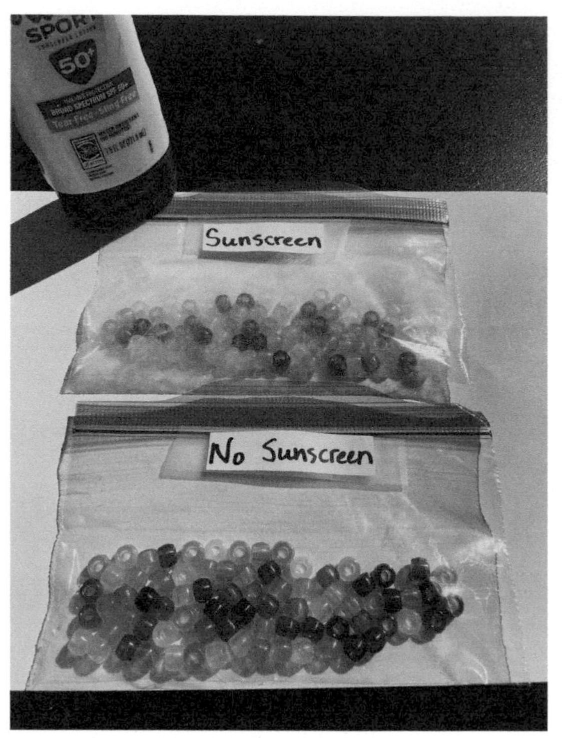

Mystery beads with and without sunscreen

skin. It should be reapplied after swimming or perspiring. Sunscreen products break down over time, so students should also be aware that there is often an expiration date printed on the bottle and that it should be discarded and replaced if expired.

evaluate

Sun Safety Tips

Give each student a copy of the Sun Safety Tip student page. Have them fill in the blank in the sentence, "When you are in the sun, wear ___________. It helps block UV light." Students can fill in the blank with answers such as sunscreen, a hat, sunglasses, or a long-sleeved shirt. Then, have students draw a picture of themselves wearing or using the protective items.

SEP: Obtaining, Evaluating, and Communicating Information
Communicate information or design ideas and/or solutions with others in oral and/or written forms using models, drawings, writing, or numbers that provide detail about scientific ideas, practices, and/or design ideas.

A sun safety tip

STEM Everywhere

Give students the STEM Everywhere student page as a way to involve their families and extend their learning. They can do the activity with an adult helper and share their results with the class. If students do not have access to the internet at home, you may choose to have them complete this activity at school.

Opportunities for Differentiated Instruction

This box lists questions and challenges related to the lesson that students may select to research, investigate, or innovate. Students may also use the questions as examples to help them generate their own questions. These questions can help you move your students from the teacher-directed investigation to engaging in the science and engineering practices in a more student-directed format.

Extra Support

For students who are struggling to meet the lesson objectives, provide a question and guide them in the process of collecting research or helping them design procedures or solutions.

Extensions

For students with high interest or who have already met the lesson objectives, have them choose a question (or pose their own question), conduct their own research, and design their own procedures or solutions.

After selecting one of the questions in this box or formulating their own questions, students can individually or collaboratively make predictions, design investigations or surveys to test their predictions, collect evidence, devise explanations, design solutions, or examine related resources. They can communicate their findings through a science notebook, at a poster session or gallery walk, or by producing a media project.

Research

Have students brainstorm researchable questions:

? What are the ingredients in sunscreen?

? How was sunscreen invented?

? What are some other UV color-changing materials?

Investigate

Have students brainstorm testable questions to be solved through science or math:

? Do sunglasses block UV light from the Sun?

? Do clouds block UV light from the Sun?

? How do sunscreens with different SPFs affect the beads' color when exposed to sunlight?

Innovate

Have students brainstorm problems to be solved through engineering:

? Can you design something to remind yourself to reapply sunscreen?

? Can you design a clothing item (hat, shirt, etc.) that uses UV beads to detect sunlight?

? Can you determine the best places to build shade structures or plant trees on the school playground?

Websites

American Sign Language Demonstration of the Sign for "Sun"
www.signasl.org/sign/sun

Sun Safety Tips for Families From the CDC
https://www.cdc.gov/cancer/skin/basic_info/sun-safety-tips-families.htm

More Books to Read

Asch, F. 2000. *The Sun is my favorite star.* New York: Gulliver Books.
Summary: This book celebrates a child's love for the Sun and explores the wondrous ways in which it helps Earth and the life upon it.

Branley, F. 1986. *What makes day and night?* New York: HarperTrophy.
Summary: This Let's-Read-and-Find-Out Science book provides a simple explanation of how the rotation of Earth causes day and night. A student activity for modeling Earth's rotation is included.

DeCristofano, C. C. 2018. *Running on sunshine: How does solar energy work?* New York: HarperCollins.
Summary: In this Let's-Read-and-Find-Out Science book, readers learn that energy from the Sun is called solar energy and that using this renewable energy resource can help keep the environment healthy.

Fowler, A. 1991. *The Sun is always shining somewhere.* Chicago: Children's Press.
Summary: This Rookie Read-About Science book gives simple examples of how the Sun is important to life on Earth, explains that the Sun is a star, and provides a simple student activity to show that Earth's rotation causes day and night and that the Sun is always shining.

Rau, D. M. 2006. *Hot and bright: A book about the Sun.* Minneapolis: Picture Window Books.
Summary: Simple text, colorful illustrations, and fun facts explain how the Sun moves, how it helps Earth, how to protect yourself from harmful rays, and more. Includes simple experiments, table of contents, a glossary, and a website with links to other safe, fun websites related to the book's content.

Sherman, J. 2003. *Sunshine: A book about sunlight.* Minneapolis: Picture Window Books.
Summary: Sunrises, sunsets, rainbows—all these things come from the Sun. Sunshine also gives us light, warmth, and food. In this book about sunlight, readers find out how the Sun creates all of our weather. Includes simple experiments, table of contents, a glossary, and a website with links to other safe, fun websites related to the book's content.

Tomecek, S. 2001. *Sun.* Washington, DC: National Geographic Society.
Summary: This information-packed book explains that the Sun is a star and that Earth's rotation causes the Sun to appear to move across the sky each day. Readers also learn how far the Sun is from Earth, what it is made of, how hot it is, and many other facts about the Sun.

Sunlight Is Special

The Sun gives off heat you can feel and light you can see. But there are some kinds of light from the Sun that you cannot see. One kind is called ultraviolet (UV) light. UV light can burn your skin or hurt your eyes.

Special beads called UV beads change color when in UV light. The brighter the colors of UV beads, the more UV light has reached them.

Mystery Beads

Name ______________________

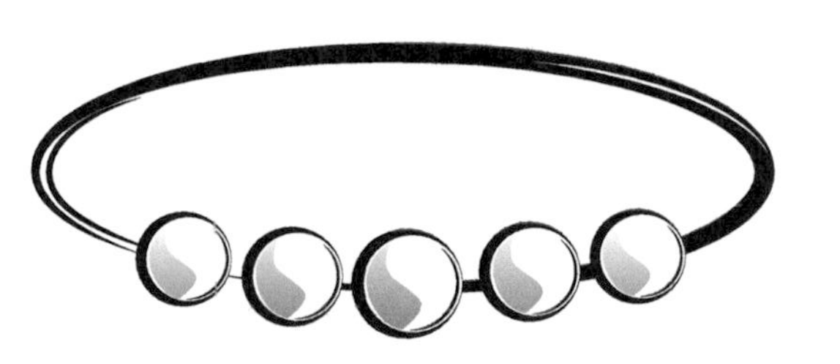

Color the mystery beads the way they look outdoors.

What Do You Think Made the Beads Change Color?

(Write or draw your answer below.)

Mystery Bead Investigations

Possible Cause	Did the Beads Change Color? Yes or No (Circle)
Heat	
Bright Light	
Water	
Cold	
Wind	
The Sun	

Thank You, Sun!

Dear Sun,

Thank you for

____

____

____

Your Friend,

____

Me in the Sunshine

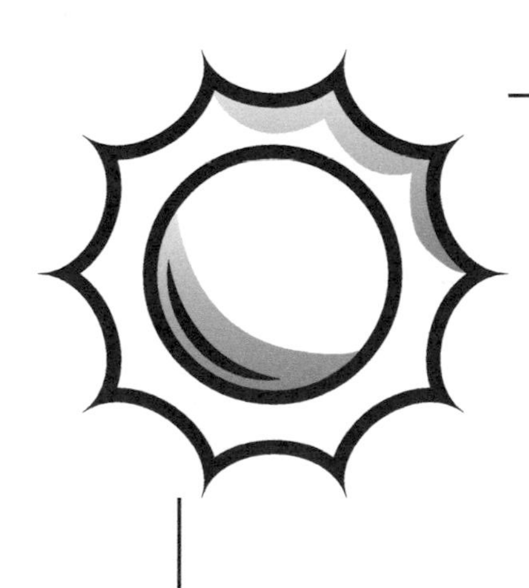

Name: ______________________

Sun Safety Tip

When you are in the Sun, wear ______________________.
It helps block UV light.

Name: ______________________________

STEM Everywhere

Dear Families,

At school, we have been learning about how the Sun provides heat and light. One part of sunlight, called *ultraviolet* (UV) light can give you a sunburn. We found out that **UV light made our "mystery beads" change color.** To find out more, ask your learner the following questions and discuss their answers:

- What did you learn?
- What was your favorite part of the lesson?
- What are you still wondering?

At home, you can watch a short video together titled "How Effective Is Your Sunscreen?" about two boys who are testing sunscreens at the beach.

Scan the QR code; go to *www.pbslearningmedia.org* and search "How Effective Is Your Sunscreen"; or go to *https://cet.pbslearningmedia.org/resource/envh10.sci.ess.eiu.sunscreen/how-effective-is-your-sunscreen*.

After watching the video, answer the following questions together:

1. What does SPF mean?

____

____

2. In the video, which sunscreen blocked out more UV light? Circle one:

SPF 4 SPF 30

3. Do you have any sunscreen in your home? If so, what is the SPF? ______